Guest Spot

Playalong for Clarinet
ALL NEW CHART HITS

Wise Publications
part of The Music Sales Group
LONDON / NEW YORK / PARIS / SYDNEY / COPENHAGEN / BERLIN / MADRID / HONG KONG / TOKYO

Published by
Wise Publications
14-15 Berners Street, London W1T 3LJ, UK.

Exclusive Distributors:
Music Sales Limited
Distribution Centre, Newmarket Road, Bury St Edmunds,
Suffolk IP33 3YB, UK.
Music Sales Pty Limited
20 Resolution Drive, Caringbah, NSW 2229, Australia.

Order No. AM1004069
ISBN 13: 978-1-78038-361-3
This book © Copyright 2011 Wise Publications,
a division of Music Sales Limited.

Edited by Jenni Norey.
Engraving and arranging supplied by Camden Music.
Top line arrangements by Christopher Hussey.
Backing tracks by Danny Gluckstein, Jeff Leach and John Maul.
Clarinet played by Howard McGill.
CD recorded, mixed and mastered by Jonas Persson.

Printed in the EU.

Your Guarantee of Quality:
As publishers, we strive to produce every book to
the highest commercial standards.
The music has been freshly engraved and the book has been
carefully designed to minimise awkward page turns and
to make playing from it a real pleasure.
Particular care has been given to specifying acid-free, neutral-sized
paper made from pulps which have not been elemental chlorine bleached.
This pulp is from farmed sustainable forests and was
produced with special regard for the environment.
Throughout, the printing and binding have been planned to
ensure a sturdy, attractive publication which should give years of enjoyment.
If your copy fails to meet our high standards,
please inform us and we will gladly replace it.

www.musicsales.com

Clarinet Fingering Chart

RK

THUMB

REED

LIGATURE

Mouthpiece

LEFT HAND

1L
2L
1ST FINGER

2ND FINGER
3L

3RD FINGER
4L

1R
2R
3R
4R

5L
6L
7L

RIGHT HAND

1ST FINGER

2ND FINGER
5R

3RD FINGER
6R
7R
8R

9R

Indicates the lower limit of the best playing range for E♭, B♭, E♭ Alto and B♭ Bass Clarinets

Indicates the upper limit of the best playing range for E♭ and B♭ Clarinets   Indicates the upper limit of the best playing range for E♭ Alto and B♭ Bass Clarinets

All About Tonight (Pixie Lott)

Words & Music by Brian Kidd, Thomas James & Tebey Ottoh

The A Team (Ed Sheeran)

Words & Music by Ed Sheeran

Leisurely and simply ♩ = 85

On %: **p**

9

Every Teardrop Is A Waterfall (Coldplay)

Words & Music by Chris Martin, Guy Berryman, Jon Buckland, Will Champion, Brian Eno

Emphatically ♩ = 118

Glad You Came (The Wanted)

Words & Music by Wayne Hector, Steve Mac & Ed Drewett

Sweetly ♩ = 112

(ride cymbal cue)

mp

Rhythmically ♩ = 127

mf

Grenade (Bruno Mars)

Words & Music by Philip Lawrence, Peter Hernandez, Christopher Brown, Ari Levine, Claude Kelly & Andrew Wyatt

Expressively ♩ = 111

Jar Of Hearts (Christina Perri)

Words & Music by Christina Perri, Drew Lawrence & Barrett Yeretsian

Last Friday Night (Katy Perry)

Words & Music by Max Martin, Lukasz Gottwald, Bonnie McKee & Katy Perry

Confidently ♩ = 126

Love Goes Down (Plan B)

Words & Music by Benjamin Drew, Eric Appapoulay, Richard Cassell & Tom Goss

Jealousy (Will Young)

Words & Music by Will Young, James Eliot & Jemima Stilwell

Tenderly ♩ = 123

Someone Like You (Adele)

Words & Music by Adele Adkins & Daniel Wilson

Smoothly, with tenderness ♩ = 68

poco rit.   a tempo

CD Track Listing

Full instrumental performances...

1. Tuning notes

2. **All About Tonight**
(Kidd/James/Ottoh) Universal/MCA Music Limited/
BMG Rights Management (UK) Limited/Copyright Control

3. **The A Team**
(Sheeran) Sony/ATV Music Publishing (UK) Limited

4. **Every Teardrop Is A Waterfall**
(Martin/Berryman/Buckland/Champion/Eno/Allen/Anderson/Castioni/
Christensen/Lagonda/Wycombe)
Harry Castioni/Alex Joerg Christensen/B Lagonda/Wycombe/Opal Music/
Universal Music Publishing Limited/Universal Music Publishing MGB Limited/
Warner/Chappell Overseas Holdings Limited

5. **Glad You Came**
(Hector/Mac/Drewett)
Warner/Chappell Music Publishing Limited/Peermusic (UK) Limited

6. **Grenade**
(Lawrence/Hernandez/Brown/Levine/Kelly/Wyatt)
Sony/ATV Music Publishing (UK) Limited/Warner/Chappell Music North
America Limited/Bug Music (Windswept Account)/EMI Music Publishing Ltd/
Bug Music Ltd

7. **Jar Of Hearts**
(Perri/Lawrence/Yeretsian) Wixen Music UK Ltd/Warner/Chappell North
America Limited/Fintage Publishing B.V.

8. **Last Friday Night**
(Martin/Gottwald/McKee/Perry) Kobalt Music Publishing Limited/
Warner/Chappell North America Limited/Kassner Associated Publishers Limited

9. **Love Goes Down**
(Drew/Appapoulay/Cassell/Goss) Universal Music Publishing PGM Limited/
Sony/ATV Music Publishing (UK) Limited

10. **Jealousy**
(Young/Eliot/Stilwell) Sony/ATV Music Publishing (UK) Limited

11. **Someone Like You**
(Adkins/Wilson) Universal Music Publishing Limited/Chrysalis Music Limited

Backing tracks only...

12. **All About Tonight**

13. **The A Team**

14. **Every Teardrop Is A Waterfall**

15. **Glad You Came**

16. **Grenade**

17. **Jar Of Hearts**

18. **Last Friday Night**

19. **Love Goes Down**

20. **Jealousy**

21. **Someone Like You**

To remove your CD from the plastic sleeve,
lift the small lip to break the perforations.
Replace the disc after use for convenient storage